Reading

for Christian Schools® 1-3

Bob Jones University Press, Greenville, South Carolina 29614

READING for Christian Schools ® 1-3
Produced in cooperation with the Bob Jones University School of Education
and Bob Jones Elementary School.

ISBN 0-89084-130-6

©1981 Bob Jones University Press
Greenville, South Carolina 29614

Printed in the United States of America

20   19   18   17   16   15   14   13   12   11   10   9   8

Contents

Mountains and Woodlands

Treasures

Hear the Music
Hear the music
Call to you.
Hear it tell you
What to do.

Roll those drums and
March those feet;
Step in time and
Keep the beat.

Clang the cymbals,
Strike the sticks;
Castanets add
Clacks and clicks.

One and two and
Three and four.
March like soldiers
Home from war.

The Bremen Town Musicians

The tired old donkey hobbled down the middle of the road. He hummed a slow but happy tune. Just this morning his master had said, "You are too old to haul things for me. You cannot stay here if you cannot work."

"I will work for myself," the donkey sang. "I will be a musician and play my fiddle in Bremen."

"What did you say?" asked a tired dog who lay by the road.

"I am going to Bremen to be a town musician. My master thinks I'm too old to work."

"My master thinks I'm too old to hunt. What will I do to feed myself?" the dog barked.

"Come with me! You can beat the drum."

4

"I will be a musician!" said the dog with a yip. The two went on down the road.

"Oh me," meowed a cat. "I am too old to catch mice."

"Would you like to sing with us? We are musicians," said the donkey and the dog.

"I will be a musician too," the cat said with a glad meow.

Soon the three musicians came upon a rooster standing in the middle of the road. "Help!" the rooster crowed. "I am too old to do anything. I will be my master's dinner."

"Be a musician. Come with us," said the donkey, the dog, and the cat.

5

"I will be a musician!" said the rooster with a cock-a-doodle-doo.

The four musicians sang as they went on down the road though they had no money, no food, and no place to sleep.

"I think I see an inn ahead. That would be a nice place to stay. We cannot reach the city by sundown," brayed the donkey.

"We can make music to get money at the inn," the dog barked. "We can get something to eat and a place to sleep too."

6

The musicians pressed on to the inn. Over the door of the inn perched a green and red bird.

"We are musicians," the four told the bird. "We want to play at the inn."

"Robbers stole every cent the innkeeper had," squawked the bird. "He cannot pay you. People fill every sleeping place in the inn. You cannot stay here. There is an old house down the road in the woods. You may stay there."

The musicians followed the dark path to the old house.

"Is this the place?" the donkey asked, putting his face up to the window.

"What do you see?" growled the dog.

"The robbers!" the donkey said.

"Oh me," the cat began to meow.

"Now, now, cat. Hush! I have a plan that will make the robbers leave this place," the rooster said.

In hushed tones he told the animals his plan. The musicians all agreed.

The donkey stood still. Up hopped the dog onto his back. With a gentle leap the cat jumped onto the dog's back. Flapping his wings, the rooster went to the top. He perched on the cat's back. The animals made a giant tower.

8

"Sing," hee-hawed the donkey.

What a braying, barking, crowing, and meowing noise they made!

The robbers jumped up! "What is that?" they yelled. "Let us get out of here!"

Away they ran as fast as they could go.

"Hooray!" yelled the musicians. They tumbled into the house.

"Look at the food!" barked the dog.

"Look at the gold!" meowed the cat.

"Look at the gems!" crowed the rooster.

The donkey hee-hawed until the house shook.

9

The musicians ate and ate until they could eat no more. They fell asleep, still thinking of the trick which had fooled the robbers.

Meanwhile the robbers sat in the cold woods. "It was silly to let something scare us," they said. "What will we do?"

"I will sneak back to the house. You wait here," said a big, tall, mean robber.

The musicians did not hear the robber come into the dark house. In the corner the robber saw the cat's glowing eyes.

The cat saw him too. He hissed and spat and clawed the robber.

The robber began to run, but the dog woke up and bit his leg. The donkey gave him a kick. The rooster crowed, "Cock-a-doodle-doo."

10

The robber raced back to the woods as fast as his legs could take him.

"What happened?" the other robbers asked.

"I was clawed by a lion that got out of its cage. A monster bit me, and then a man with a club hit me. A lady screamed, 'Get that robber.' We must get away from here quick." So they did. They never came back again.

The musicians took the gold and gems back to the innkeeper. He gave them the old house. The animals did not have to go to Bremen to become musicians. They spent their old age living in the old house in the woods. The animals made music whenever they liked.

J-O-Y

Joy liked the song Miss Adams led at the end of Bible class. The song had Joy's name in it!

Jesus and others and you,
What a wonderful way to spell joy!
Jesus and others and you,
In the life of each girl and each boy.
J is for Jesus, for He has first place,
O is for others we meet face to face;
Y is for you in whatever you do,
Put yourself third, and spell JOY!

Joy sang the song over and over in her heart as she did her schoolwork.

"J-O-Y," by Bud Metzinger, from *Salvation Songs for Children*, Number Four. Copyright 1945 by Percy B. Crawford. Reprinted by permission of Ruth Crawford Porter.

Joy reached for her coat at recess time. The name tag over her coat made her think of the song again. J-o-y. She was still thinking of the song when she got in line.

Jesus and others and you,
What a wonderful way to spell joy!

"I wish I could get a swing at recess," she thought. She looked at all the boys and girls in line before her. "The swings will all be taken," she complained to herself. The song in her heart stopped.

At lunchtime Joy waited at her seat for the noon recess to begin. The song came back to her as she thought about swinging in the fresh air. Miss Adams told the class to line up. Joy had to wait for Bill to go by with a crate of milk boxes. Again Joy found herself close to the end of the line. She grumbled to herself. The song left her heart.

At the end of art class Miss Adams began to have the class line up for the last recess. Joy's desk was ready. This time she would get a swing! The song began in her heart again.

J is for Jesus, for He has first place,
O is for others we meet face to face;
Y is for you in whatever you do,
Put yourself third and spell JOY!

Joy sat thinking about her song. "How do you get joy by being last?"

Just then Amy dropped her paint. What a sight! Purple paint went everywhere. Amy looked as if she might cry.

Joy glanced at the recess line. She could still get a swing. The song kept singing.

Put yourself third and spell JOY.

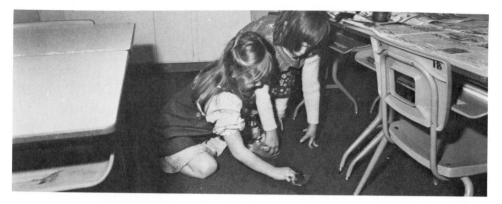

Joy thought, "I know what to do." She stopped to help Amy with the messy paint. She would not get to sing and swing today. She thought the song in her heart would stop.

Miss Adams and the rest of the class left for the playground. Joy and Amy would not be ready to play for a long time.

16

Joy wiped purple paint. Amy wiped purple paint. Purple towels went into the basket. At last Amy began to feel better. Joy was surprised to find that the song was still in her heart.

Put yourself third and spell JOY!

A Sweet Melody

It was music time in Melody Land. The leader of the orchestra was a little white stick.

The white stick tapped on the music stand. The orchestra began to play.

The fiddle family played very well at first. Then the middle fiddle lost her place and played three bad notes.

"Oh," said the trumpet. "That sounded terrible!"

"I'm surprised you could hear me," said the fiddle. "You were playing so loud I could not hear myself play."

18

"If I play loud, it is because I have a better voice," said the trumpet.

"Stop tooting your own horn," said the kettledrum. "I can play louder than anyone."

"Oh, no," said the tuba. "I can play louder than you."

The tuba began to play. The drum began to play. Each one was trying to play louder than the other.

Try as he might, the tuba could not play louder than the drum.

"Pipe down," said the flute. "You both play loud. But I can play high. I can play higher than anyone."

"Fiddlesticks," said the little fiddle. "I can play higher than you."

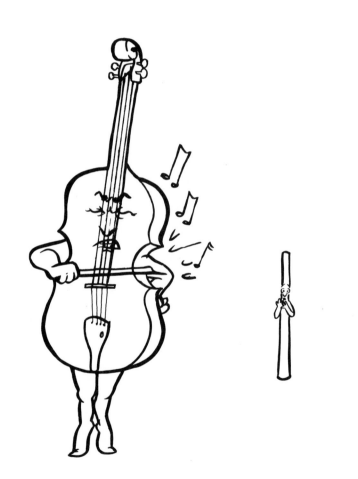

The little fiddle began to play. The flute began to play. Each one was trying to play higher than the other.

"Stop fiddling around," said the big fiddle. "You both play high, but I can play low. I can play lower than anyone."

"Oh, no," said the bassoon. "I can play lower than you."

The bassoon began to play. The big fiddle began to play. Each one was trying to play lower than the other.

The instruments were all trying to out-play each other.

The noise got louder and LOUDER and LOUDER!

The cymbals were clashing. The trumpet was blaring. The bells kept chiming in.

The clarinet screeched. The horn gave a hoot. The fiddle began to whine.

"This is not music," said the little white stick. "This is terrible!

"Stop!" he shouted. "Stop!"

The stick yelled till he was blue in the face. But no one heard.

He went to the harp. "Play something sweet," he said.

The harp began to play. She played such a sweet song that something happened.

The instruments stopped fighting!

The horn stopped hooting. The drum stopped booming. The trumpet told the fiddle he was sorry.

"I was out of tune," said the fiddle.

"We were all too sharp," said the harp.

"From now on, we will play together," said the tuba.

The white stick tapped on the music stand. Each instrument played in its own best way. And the orchestra began to play a sweet melody.

The Grasshopper and the Ants

It was the hottest day of the summer. Mr. Grasshopper lay in the shade. He played his fiddle a while. He slept a while. He played his fiddle some more. Not once did he get up to do any kind of work.

Meanwhile, out in the sun, the ants were quite busy. The biggest ant was working very hard. The middle-sized ants were working very hard. The smallest ant was working very hard too. Each was busy gathering food for the winter.

The grasshopper lay in the shade with a sneer on his face. "I'm smarter than the ants are," he thought. "It is much nicer to stay in the shade than to work in the sun."

He stood up and called to the biggest ant. "Why do you work so hard?"

"I am storing up food for the winter. You would be wise to do the same."

The grasshopper laughed. "Winter is far away. There is much time left to work. Come and play."

The ant shook his head. "Winter will come sooner than you think." He went on about his work.

Days went by. The harder the ants worked, the faster Mr. Grasshopper fiddled. By and by the days began to grow shorter. The leaves began to grow browner. The nights began to grow colder. Still Mr. Grasshopper fiddled. Still the ants worked hard.

One day it began to snow. The ground became whiter and whiter. The snow fell faster and faster. Mr. Grasshopper became colder and colder.

"I have not been so cold or hungry in many days," he thought. "I will hop around and look for food. The ants will show me where to find something to eat."

Mr. Grasshopper hopped to the field by the big oak tree. There were no ants in sight. There was no food in sight. There was just one small set of tracks in the snow. They led away from the field to a tiny house.

Mr. Grasshopper made his way through the snow to the house. A light shone from the window. Mr. Grasshopper looked inside. It was the home of the ants! The ants were gathered around the table. Food was piled high on their plates. Everyone looked warm and cozy.

Mr. Grasshopper sighed and turned away.

"The ants are smarter than I," he said. "There is a time to work and a time to play."

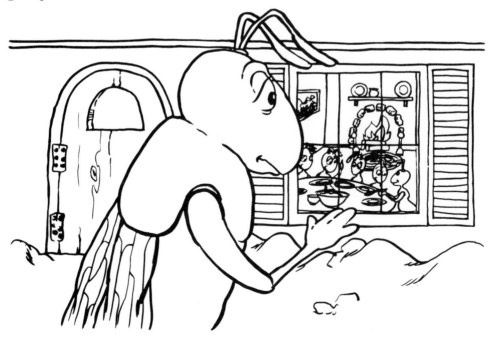

Our God Gives a Song

The men were angry. They did not like to hear Paul and Silas preach about God. They did not want to see people saved. All they wanted was money.

"These men upset the city. We can't agree with the things they teach. They must be punished!"

By then the mob was angry too. They jumped upon Paul and Silas. The rulers of the city tore the robes right off God's men.

"Beat these men!" the rulers ordered.

Many times the whips were unfairly used upon the men's backs. The people still were angry.

"Throw the men into jail!" they shouted.

Paul and Silas were cast into the dark, damp jail. The jailer did not want the men to escape. He put their feet in the stocks. The stocks were shut tight. Then the jailer left. Paul and Silas were alone in the dark, damp cell. Had God forgotten His children?

Paul and Silas did not think so. At midnight they prayed to God. They sang praises to Him. The other men in the jail heard them sing. Had God also heard them?

Suddenly the ground began to rumble. The jail began to shake. Doors opened. The chains fell off the men. God had heard His children singing. It was time for God to act.

The keeper of the jail had been sleeping. He awoke with a start. He saw the open doors.

"The men will escape. The city rulers will take my life. I will end my life myself," the jailer thought. Quickly he took out his sword.

"Stop!" commanded Paul with a loud voice. "Do not harm yourself. We are all here."

The jailer quickly snatched up a light. Trembling, he went to see Paul and Silas. What kind of God did these men have? The jailer fell down before God's men.

"Sirs, what must I do to be saved?"

"Trust in the Lord Jesus. You and your house will be saved."

The jailer was glad to hear that. Gently he washed the men's backs. Then he took Paul and Silas to his home. He gave them food to eat. He gathered his household together. He wanted to hear more about the God that could give songs in the night.

Paul and Silas were glad to speak about Jesus. That night the jailer and all of his house trusted in God. God gave them a song too. It was the song of souls set free.

"Bring my soul out of prison,
that I may praise thy name."
Psalm 142:7

The Song from Heaven

"The organ will not work. I cannot fix it." Mr. Gruber said sadly.

"We must fix it, or there will be no music," said the pastor. "I must go see the woodcutter now. Please try one more time to fix it."

He put on his warm hat and mittens. "I'll be back soon. Good-bye."

The snowy hills looked enchanting, but the pastor did not see them. The wind was cold, but the pastor did not feel it. Tonight was Christmas Eve, but there would be no music. What could he do?

"It will be a silent Christmas Eve," he said.

The poor woodcutter's house was small. The woodcutter did not mind. Today he was very happy. He had a new baby in his house.

The pastor held the tiny baby. It was fast asleep. "Dear God, thank You for this baby. Thank You, too, for the baby You sent at Christmas long ago."

The pastor walked home slowly. The cold night was silent. The bright stars were silent. Tonight was Christmas Eve.

Suddenly the pastor said, "I think I *can* do something." He ran past the silent trees to the church.

He took some paper and a pen. "I have a song," he said.

"What is all the excitement?" asked Mr. Gruber. "We still can't play the organ. Why are you glad?"

"I made up a song for Christmas, Mr. Gruber. The woodcutter's new baby made me think of the first Christmas long ago when God sent Jesus as a baby. This song tells of the baby God sent."

"I like this song. We will have a happy Christmas Eve." said Mr. Gruber.

Many weeks after Christmas Mr. Gruber came to the pastor.

"A man has come to fix the organ at last," Mr. Gruber said. "Come and hear me play."

Mr. Gruber softly played the pastor's Christmas song.

"Oh," said the man, "that is a nice song. Will you teach it to me? My home is far away. I will take the song with me. I know some children who can sing it next Christmas."

The pastor sang the song. Mr. Gruber played the organ. They were glad to teach the man.

"Lin, Joe, Amy, and Andy!" Mother called. "A man has a new song for you. Come and sing."

The children sang the song.

"Oh, Mother, we can sing this for Christmas!" said Lin.

"Yes, we will sing it every day. Then we will sing it in town. Everyone will love this song," said Mother.

One summer day the children sang in town. Someone liked the song. He ran to tell the king and queen. The king and queen asked the children to sing for them.

"Sing for the king?" asked Joe.

"Sing for the queen?" asked Lin.

"That will be great!" said Andy.

The king and queen called for the children. "Sing for us," they said.

The children sang and sang. "Silent night, holy night."

"I can't tell you how much I love that song," said the queen, smiling.

"That is a song from heaven," said the king.

Today many children sing this special song every Christmas.

A Different Kind of Music

With a bang and a clang
And a spit and a spatter,
My grandfather's heater
Begins with a clatter.

It bumps and it thumps
And it moans and it groans.
It seems that it makes
Its own funny tones.

But above I can hear
A quite different song.
My grandmother's kettle
Just whistles along.

At breakfast, at dinner,
At teatime, at noon,
It toots and it hoots out
The very same tune.

Winning Men with Music

"Dwight, are you all set to go?" asked Father. "I have to put Mother's harp in the car."

"Yes, sir," Dwight said. He jumped into the car. It was fun to go with the family to tell men about God. Father began to push the harp in beside Dwight.

"Ow!" Dwight yelled. He shielded his head with his arms. "I am too tall to fit in here with this harp. You must get someone who is short."

Father looked into the car. "I believe you are right," he laughed.

Dwight's little sister climbed into the car. She fit under the harp. The rest of the family climbed in. They barely fit. Five in the family plus a harp was a lot! With a groan the car set off. It chugged all the way into town. At last Dad stopped by a brick building.

The family scrambled out. They had an important job. They had come to tell the men about Jesus. Mother played on the harp. Dwight played his violin and sang with the other children too. Father preached to the men. He said, "Believe on the Lord Jesus Christ and you will be saved."

God used the songs. God used the preaching. Some men began to grieve over their sins. Father led these men to Jesus.

Dwight looked proudly at his father. "Someday I will win men to Jesus," he thought.

Every Sunday Dwight went to Sunday school with his family. One morning, before he could sit down, someone called to him.

"Dwight! I believe you are just the one I need for a special job. Would you be our song leader next week?"

Dwight gulped, "Me?" He was scared, but he said he would do it.

The next Sunday Dwight stood up to lead the singing. The music began. Dwight lifted his hands. Everyone sang. He waved his arms with the music. When the song was over, Dwight sat down. He was relieved that his job was done. Would song leading ever become easy?

42

Dwight liked to play the violin. One day Dwight fell and broke his collarbone. He had to wear a brace. He put his violin away. How hard it was to wait for his collarbone to heal! When it was well, he began to play his violin again.

Two years went by. Sometimes Dwight sang. Sometimes he played his violin. Then one day it happened again. Dwight slipped and broke his collarbone in the same spot. He thought, "I can't wait until my collarbone is better!" Slowly the collarbone healed. At last the doctor took off the brace. Dwight could not play his violin. His arm hurt too much. He put his violin away forever.

Today Dwight is called Dr. Gustafson. He has an important job. Do you see what he is doing? He is not playing the violin. God has another job for him to do. He wears a long black suit and a white shirt for this job. He leads all the musicians in the symphony. He waves his arms for the music to be louder. He waves them another way, and the music becomes softer. The musicians play what Dr. Gustafson's hands tell them to play. Once he thought song leading would never be easy. Now he leads a big symphony!

Sometimes Dr. Gustafson preaches like his father. He writes music too. He uses music and preaching to win people to Jesus. How glad he is that he can serve God in this way!

The Sounds of Music

Music goes high. Music goes low. Music goes fast. Music goes slow. Music is all around us. Everywhere you go, you can hear music. Some music makes you want to walk or run. Some music makes you want to jump or skip. Some music makes you just want to be quiet.

Where does good music come from? The Bible says that God is the giver of all good things. Go outside. What can you hear? Birds sing in the trees. Brooks babble over rocks. Insects hum and chirp. The wind howls, the rain patters, and the thunder rolls. All of these things have their own kind of music.

Christian people have a special kind of music too. They like to sing songs about Jesus. This kind of music is good. It praises God. It helps them tell others about Jesus. When they are sad, it makes their hearts glad. This music lets them tell

God what is in their hearts. It helps them understand more about God.

What are some musical things that you can do? You can memorize a song. This makes it yours. You can make up a tune to a Bible verse and teach it to your family. You can sing while you work. You can read Psalm 150 and list all the musical instruments named there. Finally, you can pray to God and thank Him for the gift of music.

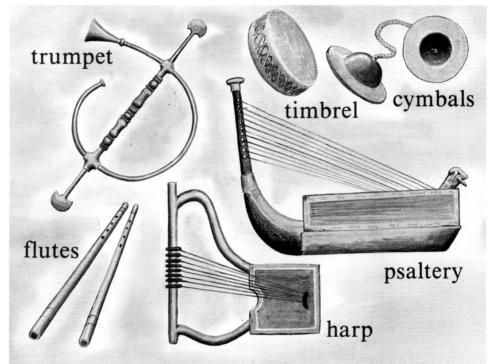

trumpet

timbrel

cymbals

flutes

psaltery

harp

Music in Spain

(a true story)

Marisita nudged Cati. "Mrs. Allen has her guitar. She will play it for Bible club."

"I hope we will hear some new hymns."

Song time seemed too short. Cati and Marisita loved to sing. Over and over the words of the hymn made them think. The words said that Jesus had died for them. The words also said that Jesus loved them. In the Bible story Mrs. Allen told them that Jesus could save them.

"Come and talk to me if you need to be saved," Mrs. Allen said.

Marisita walked over to see Mrs. Allen.

Mrs. Allen prayed with Marisita. Then Marisita prayed. She asked God to forgive her sins. She became a Christian.

Cati saw Marisita pray. She needed to be saved, too, but she was shy. She did not want to talk to this lady from across the sea.

Marisita ran to tell Cati of her new belief in Jesus. "You must believe too," Marisita said.

Mrs. Allen began to play a hymn on her guitar. Cati hid her face behind Marisita's back, but she sang the words softly.

Mrs. Allen played all of the song. Cati forgot to be scared. She stopped hiding and walked closer to Mrs. Allen. "Would you like to become a Christian?" Mrs. Allen asked.

"Yes," Cati nodded. She prayed with Mrs. Allen.

One day Mr. Allen said, "Cati and Marisita, would you like to play the guitar? I will teach you if you like."

After Bible club Marisita and Cati took turns playing the guitar. Soon they played very well. They asked many of the children from school to come to Bible club. Marisita and Cati played the special music. The hymns they played made the children think about how God loved them. The words told them that Jesus had died for them. Some of them saw that they needed to be saved, just like Marisita and Cati.

50

Mountains and Woodlands

The Three Billy Goats Gruff

(a folk drama)

Characters:  Narrator—Penny Wren

Little Billy Goat

Big Billy Goat

Middle Billy Goat

Troll

Penny Wren: Once upon a time three Billy Goats Gruff lived on a grassy hill.

Little Billy Goat: I am the little Billy Goat Gruff. I like to munch green grass for breakfast.

Middle Billy Goat: I am the middle Billy Goat Gruff. I like to snack on green grass for lunch.

Big Billy Goat: I am the big Billy Goat Gruff. I like to feast on green grass for dinner.

52

Penny Wren: The three billy goats soon nibbled every blade of green grass on the hill.

Big Billy Goat: We will have to go to the mountains now.

Middle Billy Goat: The grass is long and green there.

Little Billy Goat: The sky is blue and cool there.

Penny Wren: Off they skipped to the mountains. The three Billy Goats Gruff had to cross over a bridge to get there. But danger lurked at the bridge.

Troll: I'm a hungry old troll,
And I need to get fatter;
These skinny, thin wrists
Are the proof of the matter.

Penny Wren: He is the mean, hungry old troll. I fly high when I pass his bridge.

Troll: From the point of my long nose
To the end of my claw toes,
I am a mean old troll.

Penny Wren: Do the Billy Goats Gruff know the mean troll hides under the bridge? Here comes the little billy goat now.

Sound effects (two children): Clip-clop, clip-clop!

Troll: Who is that clip-clopping over my bridge?

Little Billy Goat: I am the little Billy Goat Gruff. I am going to the mountains for breakfast.

Troll: You cannot cross my bridge! I will eat you up.

Little Billy Goat: I am just a little billy goat. Soon the middle billy goat will come. He is much bigger. Wait for him. Please let me cross.

Troll: Go up to the mountains and get fat. I will catch you when you come back.

Penny Wren: The little billy goat ran away as quickly as he could. Here comes the middle billy goat. What will he do?

Sound effects (four children): Trip-trap, trip-trap!

Troll: Who is that trip-trapping over my bridge?

Middle Billy Goat: I am the middle Billy Goat Gruff. I am going to the mountains for lunch at noon.

Troll: You cannot cross my bridge! I will eat you up.

Middle Billy Goat: I am just the middle billy goat. Soon the big billy goat will come. Wait for him. Please let me cross.

Troll: Go up to the mountains and get fat. I will catch you when you come back.

Penny Wren: Away to the mountains ran the middle billy goat. At last the big billy goat is coming. Will the troll eat him up?

Sound effects (everyone): Thump, thud, thump, thud!

Troll: Who is that thump-thudding over my bridge?

Big Billy Goat: I am the big Billy Goat Gruff! I am going to the mountains for dinner.

Troll: I am the mean old troll. I will catch you and eat you up.

Big Billy Goat: Come, if you dare. I have two horns to push you with. I have four feet to kick you with. You cannot eat me.

Penny Wren: The troll turned red with rage. With a thump and a thud the big Billy Goat Gruff pushed him off the bridge. Through the air and into the stream went the troll. I heard him mumble as he floated away.

Troll: Each goat was too small,

And I wanted one bigger.

Now they feast on the hill,

And my wrists get still thinner.

Penny Wren: There is no more danger at the bridge, for the troll has floated away. The Billy Goats Gruff still climb the mountains to eat the long green grass under the cool blue sky.

The Rocky Mountains

Have you ever played king of the mountain?

In the western United States, the Rocky Mountains are king. On a clear day, you can see the mountains one hundred miles away.

Would you like to visit the Rocky Mountains? Read with me and I will take you there.

On the lower slopes, the grass is cool and green. Waterfalls splash over mossy rocks. Wildflowers bloom pink and white.

We sit by a quiet stream and wait. Sh-h-h! Here they come. A deer and her white-spotted fawn have stopped to drink.

Our road winds like a snake up the side of a mountain. It is a long, long way to the top. The ground seems to climb straight up into the sky.

Far below us we can see a deep valley

called a canyon. From up here the trees in the canyon look like little blades of grass. The rushing river looks like a tiny silver ribbon winding through the canyon.

Now we are at the very tip-top of the mountain. We do not see any trees here.

It is too cold for trees. B-r-r-r! It is too cold for me! Even in summer, these mountain peaks have snow on them.

In the wintertime, the mountains huddle under a blanket of snow. The woods wear a coat of winter white.

If you lived in a cabin on the mountain, you could be snowbound. You could not go anywhere. The roads would be blocked by snow.

Long ago, horse-drawn sleds delivered mail during the winter. Like the mailmen, the horses wore snowshoes. The horses did not seem to mind, and the people were glad to get their mail.

People also traveled on long skis made of spruce or fir. They put wax on the bottoms of their skis. Zoom! Down the hill they would fly at sixty miles an hour.

Today many people still like to ski. They use shorter skis that cannot go as fast. But it is still a lot of fun to race down the mountain.

Other people like to pile up like logs on a sled. Hop on and we'll take a ride. Whoosh! The sled whips down the side of the mountain. If you are on the bottom, it is your job to steer!

Did you like our trip to the Rocky Mountains? Maybe we can visit again sometime.

Attack on Boone's Fort

(a true story)

Daniel Boone looked over the wall of the fort. The fighting had stopped again. What was going on? He looked at the river. Something was wrong.

The water was muddy downstream. Upstream it was clear. Someone was throwing dirt into the river. Where was the dirt coming from?

Daniel climbed the tower to take a look. He did not like what he saw.

The Indians were digging a tunnel to the fort.

"What will we do?" said the settlers.

"We will dig a tunnel too," said Daniel. "Our tunnel will run under the cabins along the wall. The Indian tunnel will have to cross ours. Maybe we can stop them there."

The settlers worked night and day. They

took turns digging and fighting. They did not get much sleep.

Sometimes the Indians attacked at night. Finally they crept up to the fort and shot burning arrows over the wall.

The settlers did not have much water. They tried to beat out the flames. It was hopeless.

The fort was on fire!

The settlers prayed for a miracle. It began to rain. The fire sputtered. The flames began to flicker and die. The settlers were thankful.

It rained all night. It rained the next day.

Daniel went down to look at the tunnel. The men had stopped digging. "Listen!" they whispered.

Daniel listened. He heard a noise. Chink! Chink! It was the sound of shovels.

The Indians were digging closer and closer. How long would it be before they reached the fort?

The rain fell harder. That night it turned into a blinding storm.

The wind howled. The rain came down in sheets. The thunder rolled and crashed. Lightning flashed across the sky.

66

The settlers were afraid. They could not see or hear anything over the storm.

Soon the Indians would push through the tunnel. They would rush to the gate at the same time and swarm over the walls of the fort.

The settlers were brave. They would put up a good fight. But how could thirty men stop four hundred Indians?

Daniel ordered the men along the wall to keep a lookout.

The men huddled against the logs. The cold, wet rain whipped their faces.

They had been thankful for the rain at first. But why had God sent this terrible storm?

Grimly they waited and prayed for the morning.

Just before dawn, the storm stopped. Everything was suddenly quiet.

No shots were fired. There was no attack on the fort.

The sun came out. A bird began to sing.

Daniel was puzzled. Where were the Indians?

"Maybe they gave up," said one of the settlers.

"But why?" said Daniel.

There was a shout from the wall. "Look! Look at the Indian tunnel!"

The settlers looked. They began to cheer. Daniel looked out over the wall.

He was surprised by what he saw! The rain last night had soaked the ground.

The tunnel had caved in.

The Indians had left.

Mountain Friends

The morning sun shone on Pete's hair, making it look even redder than before.

"Look at that!" Dan exclaimed. "A butter-fly is sitting on your head!"

Pete grinned. "I have many little friends. My red hair must look like a flower to them. It's nice except when a bee thinks I'm a flower."

Dan laughed. He was beginning to think it might be fun to live on the mountain. Yesterday he didn't have any friends. Now he had Pete. Pete was twelve years old. He knew all about the mountain. Today he was going to show Dan some special things.

The path turned away from the sunny field into the shaded woods. Pete stopped suddenly.

"Look there," he said, pointing.

A spiderweb stretched between the branches of a small tree. Dew drops on it sparkled in the morning sunlight. In the middle of the web sat a little black spider.

Green plants that looked like wee umbrellas were growing in the shade.

"Those are mayapples," said Pete. "Indians used to boil the roots. Then they drank the water to make them well."

Dan followed Pete on through the woods.

70

"Here is my friend jack-in-the-pulpit," said Pete, stooping. Dan looked closely. "It does look like a little man standing in a pulpit ready to preach."

The boys walked on. Pete showed Dan a pitcher plant next. Its leaves formed a vase which was filled with water. Insects caught in there became food for the plant.

71

Rat-a-tat-tat! Rat-a-tat-tat!

Dan was puzzled. "That sounds like someone hammering, but no one is near."

Pete looked up at the tops of the oak trees. "There is the little carpenter," he whispered. He shaded his eyes and pointed to a sunny treetop.

The noisy woodpecker saw the boys at the same time. He circled to the other side of the tree and peeked at the boys from his place of safety.

"Come on," said Pete. "Let's leave the hole-driller to find more insects. The sun tells me it's about time to go home. I want to introduce you to one more set of friends."

Pete climbed a big beech tree. Its dead top was filled with woodpecker holes. He pounded on it with his fist. Sleepy little faces popped out from everywhere. Soon the air was filled with flying squirrels leaping to nearby trees.

Pete scrambled down the tree. A wood frog hopped across his foot into the shadows of the tree trunk.

"See how short the shadows are. The sun is nearly overhead. It's lunch time. Come on, Dan, let's go!"

The two boys ran down the trail through the woods. "It is nice to live on a mountain," Dan thought, "and to have so many friends."

These Are God's Woods

These are God's woods,
    and here I run
When school is out
    and work is done.

A fir tree guards
    my pathway's door
And sprinkles needles
    on the floor.

The tallest one
    of all the trees
Whispers softly
    in the breeze.

Its branches spread
    and make a place
Where busy squirrels
    and chipmunks race.

And as I circle
    round this tree,
I think, "How great
    our God must be!"

The Little Chipmunk in the Woods

It was summer in the mountain woods. The sun shone brightly on each wild flower. A little chipmunk sat near an oak tree. He did not see the flowers. He just saw a blue jay flying high in the sky.

"Look! Look!" boasted the blue jay as he landed on a branch. "I can see the other side of the mountain. What a grand sight! Little chipmunk, you are too small to see what I can see."

The little chipmunk sighed. "I want to see grand sights too. I will look up high to see all I can."

An old owl looked down from the tree. "Who but you can see small things near the ground? You are just the right size."

But the little chipmunk did not listen. He scampered away with his head held high. He wanted to see a big mountain far away.

He passed a spider spinning her web in an old tree stump.

She called out as he came near. "Mr. Chipmunk, look at my web. It is thin and dainty, but it is strong too. I will catch a bug in it!"

The little chipmunk did not stop to look. He could not be bothered with a spider and her web. There were grand things to be seen. He stretched his neck high. On into the woods he ran.

A baby bird saw the chipmunk scurry by.

"Please stop to see my colored wings.

They took me on my first trip today," he chirped.

The little chipmunk held his head high. He went on by. A baby bird could not be a grand sight.

The chipmunk ran fast through the mountain woods. He saw no grand sights. He grew tired of holding his head high. Sadly he made his way back to the oak tree.

There sat the blue jay near a hole in the ground. He shook his head from side to side. "Please help me, Mr. Owl. I lost my nut. It rolled down this small hole. I cannot reach my nut."

The old owl hooted to the little chipmunk, "Who but you can fit in that small hole? You are just the right size."

The little chipmunk slipped into the hole. Out he came again with the nut. The blue jay took the nut and flew back up into the tree.

The little chipmunk began to think. "Maybe sometimes it is good to be small, but I still cannot see grand sights."

Just then a dark cloud blocked out the sun. The wind shook the tree. Rain began to fall in the mountain woods.

The little chipmunk looked for a shelter from the rain. "Where can I go to stay dry?"

The old owl hooted again. "Who but you can hide in that small hole? You are just the right size."

So the little chipmunk hid in the hole.

At last the rain stopped. The sunshine beamed on the mountain woods. A tiny head poked out of the hole.

The little chipmunk looked all around. He looked at each wild flower. He saw the drops of rain sparkling on the spider's web. He saw the bright wings of the baby bird. Then the little chipmunk was glad that he was small. There were many lovely sights right near the ground.

The old owl hooted. "Who? Who is just the right size?"

Sleepy Heads

Faith was still asleep when Joy went to tell her baby sister good-bye. "I wish you and Mother could come," she whispered. "I'll see you late tonight."

Out in the car Paul was already curled up in the back. "You can sit with Dad," yawned Paul. "I'm not through sleeping yet."

Joy couldn't understand how anyone could sleep on such an exciting day. "Dad, who opened Mr. Smith's cabin for the season before we started doing it?" asked Joy.

"His children helped him when they were your age. He wrote from out West to ask if we could help out again this year," said Dad. "Paul, are you awake? Let's pray before we start the trip."

Dad led in prayer. Then Paul settled down to sleep. Dad said, "Joy, dawn is a good time to look for animals." She sat up tall, eager to see one.

Several hours later Dad turned the car onto the gravel road that led up to Smith's cabin. Joy had still not seen an animal. Paul awoke just as the car stopped in the sandy driveway.

"The cabin seems to be asleep," Joy whispered. Piles of leaves blanketed the deck. Big wooden shutters were closed tightly over the windows. The clearing was empty of both people and animals.

"We will wake this place up!" said Dad, getting out of the car. Before long the cabin was a busy place. The wooden shutters were opened. Leaves were swept from the deck. The three Heaths swept and scrubbed and fixed.

Paul and Dad were coming in with a load of firewood when Joy called down from above. "Not all the cabin is awake yet! Come and see!" she said. Paul and Dad climbed the ladder to the loft.

There was Joy, looking at a nest of baby squirrels fast asleep.

"They look just like baby Faith did when I said good-bye to her this morning," Joy giggled.

"They can't stay here, can they, Dad?" Paul asked.

"No, if the mother does not find a new home for them we will have to find one for her. You will have to help me find her secret door into this cabin."

On the way home that night Paul sat next to Dad. "Dusk is a good time to look for animals," Dad reminded him.

This time Joy was in the back. "I think it is better to find sleeping animals," she yawned. "Good night."

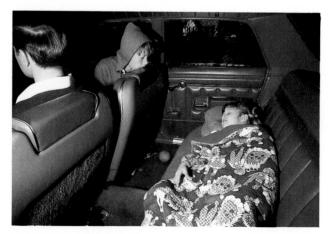

The Contest on the Mountain

Angry King Ahab pointed his finger at God's man, Elijah. "You are bringing much harm to my people. Their cattle die. Their crops die. There is no water to drink."

Elijah boldly answered the king. "It is your fault that there is no rain. You have not obeyed the true God. You follow the false god Baal. Gather your people together on Mount Carmel. We will have a contest to see who is the true God."

So Ahab gathered his people together on the mountain top. Elijah stood alone, but he knew that God was with him. He was not afraid.

Elijah said, "We will build two altars. Each of us will make an offering. The true God will send fire."

Ahab's men made an altar to Baal. They began to pray, asking their god to send fire on their altar. They prayed from morning until noon. Nothing happened.

Elijah spoke to Ahab's men. "Pray more," he said.

They prayed harder, leaping around the altar. Still nothing happened.

"Try again. Maybe Baal is sleeping," Elijah mocked. "Maybe your god is talking or taking a trip."

The men prayed all day long, jumping and leaping and making much noise. Still the fire did not come. The god of Ahab did not answer.

Then Elijah took twelve big stones and began to build an altar. He dug a ditch around the altar.

"Fill four barrels with water and pour it on the altar," Elijah commanded the people. "Do it the second time," he said. They did it the second time. "Do it the third time." They did it the third time.

The ground around the altar became muddy. The water filled up the ditch around the altar.

Elijah kneeled and prayed. "Lord, I know that You are the true God. You can do anything. Please show these people that You are God."

Then the fire of the Lord fell! It burned up the offering. It burned up the twelve stones and the wood. It licked up the water in the ditch.

The people fell on their faces. Now they, too, knew that Elijah's God was the true God.

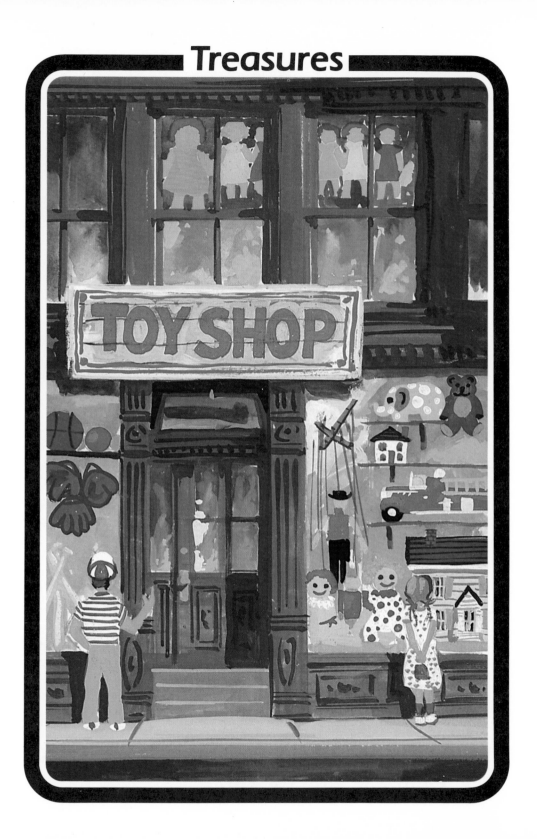

Treasures Old and New

(a true story)

Drew held his mother's hand tightly. His feet sank into the thick red carpet. Big paintings in heavy gold frames hung on all the walls around him.

"This is where I work, Drew. Every morning I tell people about the paintings. The paintings are treasures."

90

The next day after school Drew could hardly wait to show Mother his picture. "Mother," he called, running in from the bus, "I made a picture for you!"

Drew looked eagerly at Mother's face. "Can you see the train and the train man? Will you take this picture to your art museum?"

"Drew, all the paintings at the art museum are about God," said Mother. "There are no train paintings. I like your picture. I would like to keep it here at home."

The following afternoon Drew held his new picture with care. The bus seemed to go too slowly today. Drew could hardly wait to show Mother his new picture. When the bus turned onto Green Street, he could see Mother in the yard with little Brad.

"This time I made a picture about God," Drew said. He handed Mother a paper. "You can take this picture to the art museum where you work."

Mother bent over so Brad could see too. "Tell me about the picture, Drew," she said.

Drew pointed to each thing in the picture. "This is Jesus, and this is the manger. A cow and a lamb are looking at the baby."

Brad pointed to the baby in the picture. "Jesus," he said. Then he pointed to the lamb and the cow.

Brad liked the picture. Mother liked it too. "Is it a treasure?" Drew asked.

Mother said, "Yes, it is a treasure. It is a treasure to me. It is a treasure to Brad. We will make a place in our home for treasures like this."

That night at the supper table Drew showed his pictures to Dad. Mother explained her plan for an art museum at home for special treasures.

Dad made a special place for Drew's pictures. He put a bulletin board down low so Drew and Brad could see. He put it in the kitchen where Mother could see it when she worked at home.

Drew stood looking at the pictures with Mother. Dad had fixed a nice frame around each one. "This is just like the art museum," Mother said. "I can tell people who visit our home about the pictures. These pictures are our treasures!"

Faith Hides a Treasure

Mother looked at the big, gray rain clouds. "The sun will not shine today," she said. "You will have to play inside. What can you do when it is raining?"

"I can build my airplane," said Paul.

"I can color my book," said Joy.

"I can work on my puzzle," said Mark.

"Faith can play in her playpen. She will be glad you are here," said Mother.

Paul put the wings on his airplane. Then he made it fly upside down. "Vr-room," he said. Faith laughed.

Joy colored a puppy. "Ruff, ruff," she said. Faith laughed again.

Mark put his puzzle together. Then he took it apart and put it in the box. He shook the box. The puzzle rattled. Faith laughed and laughed.

"My airplane is done. I will go help Mother," said Paul.

"Me too," said Joy.

"I smell something good. I will help Mother too," said Mark.

Mother was holding something wrapped in silver paper.

"What did you make?" asked Paul.

"I baked a treasure," Mother said.

"Can we eat the treasure?" asked Joy.

"This will be a hidden treasure," said Mother. "If you find it, you may eat it."

"What is the treasure?" asked Mark.

"It is gold cookies!" Mother said. "You must stay in here while Faith and I hide the treasure." Mother left the room with the treasure.

"How can we find the treasure?" Mark asked Paul and Joy.

Paul thought for a while. "We will have to look everywhere," he said.

Joy thought too. "Our noses can help us find this treasure," she said.

"I will be a good treasure hunter!" said Mark. "I will look high and low. I will smell the treasure and find where it is hidden!"

Just then Mother came back. "Time to go find the gold cookie treasure," she said.

Off went the treasure hunters to find the hidden gold.

Paul looked in the hall. He sniffed and sniffed. "No gold treasure here!" he said.

Joy looked on the bookshelf. She sniffed and sniffed too. "No gold treasure here!" she said.

Mark looked by the window. He sniffed and sniffed some more. "No gold treasure here!" he said.

The children sat down to think. Where could the gold cookie treasure be?

"Where did you hide the treasure, Faith?" Mark asked.

Faith laughed.

"I wish Faith could tell us!" said Joy.

Still Faith just laughed.

Paul looked at Faith. "Faith *is* telling us!" he said. "Look, there is the gold treasure!"

The children reached under Faith's play-pen. Out came the treasure.

"M-m-m," they said. "Treasure hunting is fun."

Through a Sea Shell's Door

To be small enough,
only tall enough
to step through a sea shell's door
would be fun, I think,
to go clink, clink, clink
down the pink, pink porcelain floor.

To go through the halls
with the pearly walls
and the twirly, curly ways
would be fun, and oh,
then I'd get to know
how the sea-shell organ plays!

by Aileen Fisher

"Through a Sea Shell's Door," from *Runny Days, Sunny Days,* by Aileen Fisher. New York: Abelard-Schuman, 1958. Reprinted by permission of the author.

Mary's Treasure

(based on John 12)

"Jesus is coming for dinner!" Mary said, running in the door.

Martha jumped up. "Help me, Mary. We must clean the house and bake before He comes."

Martha's hands flew—dusting, sweeping, cooking and baking. Mary helped, but her feet kept walking to the door where she could look for Jesus.

Soon He would come. Mary saw how Martha had cleaned the house until it sparkled. She smelled the good food Martha was making. Mary wanted to do something special for Jesus, too, but Martha had done everything.

Then Mary thought of something she could do. She had a special treasure she could give to Jesus.

"Jesus is here!" Martha called.

Mary hurried to the door. Lazarus was bringing Jesus and His disciples inside. Martha was putting dinner on the table.

Mary took out the little jar that held her treasure. As Jesus sat down, she broke it open.

Mary poured the ointment from the jar onto the bare feet of Jesus. A lovely smell filled the house as she wiped His feet with her hair.

"What is that smell?" everyone asked.

Jesus knew it was Mary's treasure.

Judas saw Mary wash Jesus' feet with the sweet-smelling ointment. He became angry. "We could have sold that for a lot of money," he grumbled.

Jesus answered, "Leave Mary alone. She has done this for Me. I must die soon. I am glad Mary has given Me her treasure. Now I know she loves Me."

How thankful Mary's heart was! She had given her treasure to Jesus. And Jesus was pleased.

Yoshiko Decides

(a true story)

Yoshiko slipped off her shoes before entering the house. Silently the paper door closed behind her. The small, black-haired Japanese girl hurried to the low table. She bowed to Grandmother before sitting on the mat floor. Mother was pouring the green tea.

"Yoshiko," said Mother quietly, "something is on your mind."

Yoshiko sighed. "Keiko is on a fishing trip with her father. Today is not Bible Club day. I have nothing to do."

"You are too shy," Mother said gently. "You need to make more friends. Father thinks it might help you to take kendo. It will teach you to be bolder. Tomorrow you can begin."

After school the next day, Yoshiko started down the road. Her feet hurried past the rice paddies. They went slower past the fishing boats. They finally stopped before the door of her new school. It was not too late to run home.

"Japanese people do not run away," said Yoshiko. She took a deep breath, held her head high, and opened the door. Other children were already dressed for their lessons. Yoshiko rushed to get ready. She did not want to be different. She did not want people to stare at her because she was late.

Class began. The children bowed first to the god shelf. Then they bowed to the teacher. He told the children it was important to bow to the god shelf. Those who did not would not do well at kendo.

After that first week, Yoshiko began to look forward to her Saturday kendo lessons. It was fun to shout and leap with her stick. Sometimes Yoshiko was the winner of the game. Sometimes she was the loser. Sometimes the game was a tie.

Whatever happened, Yoshiko enjoyed telling the Bible club teacher. After school on Mondays, Yoshiko hurried down the road. She went past the rice paddies, past the fishing boats, past the kendo school, right to the teacher's house. Miss Cochran was always ready to listen to Yoshiko.

And Yoshiko was always eager to listen to the Bible stories. She had just become a Christian at Bible club. Now the Bible and kendo were more important to Yoshiko than anything.

One day, though, Miss Cochran told a Bible story that bothered Yoshiko. After Bible club the Japanese girl left quickly. She wanted to be alone. She wanted to think about Daniel's three friends who would not bow before a false god. They were thrown into the fire!

Slowly Yoshiko walked past the kendo school. She stopped and looked back at the door of the school. "Kendo is important," thought Yoshiko. "The teacher said I cannot do well if I do not bow to the god shelf. My friends all bow."

Yoshiko walked past the fishing boats.

She walked on past the rice paddies to her home. Slipping off her shoes at the door, Yoshiko entered her house. Mother was putting flowers on the table.

"Yoshiko," said Mother quietly, "something is on your mind."

Yoshiko sighed. "Kendo is important to me. But Jesus is important too. It is not right for a Christian to bow to the god shelf. What can I do?"

"You must ask the Lord to show you," answered Mother. "Then we will talk to Father."

That night Yoshiko tossed and turned on her mat. She could not sleep. "Daniel's friends did not mind being different," she thought. "It was more important to them to obey God than to live. I must obey God too. I will not bow to the god shelf anymore. Jesus is more important to me than kendo."

Yoshiko fell asleep. She had decided.

A Pocket of Things

A pocket's quite a handy thing
To store my nails and sticks and string,

A place where no one else can see
The treasures that belong to me.

My cars and trucks and rubber bands
Don't feel quite safe just in my hands,

For everybody else can see
The treasures that belong to me.

But in my pockets I can hide
A snake or frog that wants a ride,

A bluebird's egg found on the walk,
A snail, a pen, a piece of chalk,

A shell, a ring, a smooth round stone,
A whistle, block, or doggy bone.

And so I never need to fear.
My pockets hold my treasures near!

The Best Treasure of All

(a true story)

"You must be good today," Karl told the baby. "Our Christian friend from the United States is coming. He is bringing us Bibles."

The baby was much too little to understand, but Karl knew what was happening.

Mother picked up the baby. "Prayer time, Karl," she reminded him.

Karl sat by Father. "Why does Mr. Paulus have to smuggle Bibles to us?" he asked.

"The law in our land will not let us have Bibles," said Father.

"But we have prayed for a Bible for years," said Karl.

"Yes, and God has heard our prayers. He is giving us a great treasure," said Father.

Karl folded his hands. "Dear Jesus," he

prayed, "do not let anyone catch Mr. Paulus and take away the Bibles."

Mr. Paulus knew the family was praying for him. He stopped the van at a big metal gate. He looked at the blankets hiding the Bibles. Would the Bibles be safe? Guards were coming to check his van. If they peeked under the blankets, they would see the Bibles! They would not let him come into their land.

"Dear God," he prayed, "help me take these Bibles to the Christians who need them. They have prayed for Bibles a long, long time."

The guards looked at the outside of the van. They looked at some papers Mr. Paulus gave them. Then they let him go through the gate. God had answered prayer!

Mr. Paulus drove a long way.

At last he backed the van into the driveway. "The Bibles have come! Our friend is here!" Karl whispered excitedly.

"Children," Father said, "there are many Bibles. We can give some to our friends. Right now we must get the Bibles into the house."

"Can we help?" Karl asked.

"Yes," Father said. "You must play in the grass by the van. We can bring the Bibles in behind you."

Mother said, "Take the baby with you and be careful. You must not be too quiet or too noisy. No one must suspect that we have Bibles."

The children sang to the baby. They played games with the baby. Karl was very careful not to be too quiet or too noisy. No one would suspect that he was helping to smuggle Bibles!

Again and again Father and Mr. Paulus took bags of Bibles into the house.

The baby laughed and played. Karl took the baby's hand and whispered, "I am glad you are too little to know what is happening! If you were bigger, you might be too quiet or too noisy."

At last the Bibles were safe. The family thanked their Christian friend.

"Dear God," Father prayed, "thank You for the treasure You gave us today, in Jesus' name. Amen."

The baby gurgled and smiled at Karl. "When you get older, I will read our treasure to you. You will love our Bible too," said Karl.

116

The Case of the Missing Treasure

Blue, orange, red, green, and yellow gems sparkled and glistened on the castle walls. Slug pointed out a special new gem to Starfish, a thorny newcomer to the Sea Reef Community.

Starfish whistled. "This is much more magnificent than I ever dreamed! Does anyone guard this treasure?"

Slug answered carelessly. "There is no one around that would steal it, except for Parrotfish. We keep a close eye on him. Our king, Giant Triton, is not here. Come and meet the queen."

Queen Triggerfish was quite charmed by Starfish. "I am glad to meet you," she said, fluttering her fins. "I don't know when the king will be back. He will want to meet you though."

Starfish smiled smugly. He bowed to the queen. Then he left the castle to find a place to sleep.

The next morning the underwater community was in a big hubble-bubble! Someone had stolen part of the treasure!

Parrotfish fled to his cave. He knew that he would be the first one suspected.

Crab held up his claw to silence the crowd. "Some gems are missing, but there are no teeth marks left on the castle wall," he said in a crabby voice. "Therefore we know that Parrotfish did not take the treasure."

The crowd nodded their heads. Crab was right.

"What we do not know," said Crab, "is who *did* take the treasure."

The angry fish murmured. Again Crab held up his claw. "I have a plan. Each fish will take a turn guarding the treasure."

The crowd clapped. It was a good plan.

Slug hurried to wake up Starfish.

"Something terrible has happened! Part of the treasure has been stolen. You are a newcomer here, but you still must help. You must take a turn guarding the treasure."

"I will be glad to guard the treasure at night—if no one minds, that is," said Starfish slyly.

So each member of the Sea Reef Community began to take turns guarding the castle's treasure. Everything went well the first day. It seemed as if the plan would work.

The following morning Slug found Starfish sleeping next to the castle.

"Wake up!" yelled Slug. "Someone has stolen more of the treasure!"

Members of the Sea Reef Community came from everywhere. Starfish sat up, rubbing his eyes.

"I didn't mean to fall asleep," he apologized.

Big empty spots dotted the castle walls. Over half of the sparkling colored gems were missing.

"Go find Giant Triton," ordered Crab. "The king will know what to do."

Tuna sped away quickly. He was a fast swimmer, but it might take days to find the king.

Starfish tried to look sad. "I will guard the treasure more closely tonight."

Slowly the crowd disappeared. The treasure was not disturbed again that day.

The sun shone brightly the next morning on Starfish, who was sleeping again.

"Wake up!" yelled Slug. "More of the treasure has been stolen!"

A large, murmuring crowd gathered around the nearly bare castle walls.

"Get the thief!" they yelled. But they

did not know who the thief was.

Lantern Eye, Trumpetfish, and Crab huddled together talking. At last Crab spoke up.

"Everyone must go home," he ordered. "We will keep on guarding the treasure as we planned."

Starfish snickered and then went back to sleep. He would guard the treasure again that night.

The night was dark as Starfish crept slowly over the castle walls.

Suddenly a light flashed on Starfish.

"There is the thief!" yelled Lantern Eye. "Sound the alarm!"

Trumpetfish blew the loudest alarm he could make.

"Grab him! Grab him!" shouted Crab.

"We can't!" screamed Slug. "He is too spiny. He will slash us to pieces!"

The fish fell silent. There was nothing they could do. Giant Triton alone could stop the thief, and he was not here.

Starfish laughed wickedly. He turned and started off through the black water with the castle's gems.

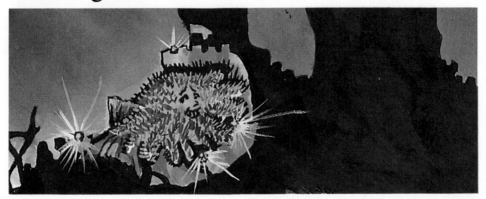

Suddenly he stopped. Out of the night came the returning Giant Triton.

The crowd went wild! The thief was caught! The treasure was safe!

As the sun rose on Sea Reef Community that morning, the blue, orange, red, green, and yellow gems once again glistened on the castle walls.